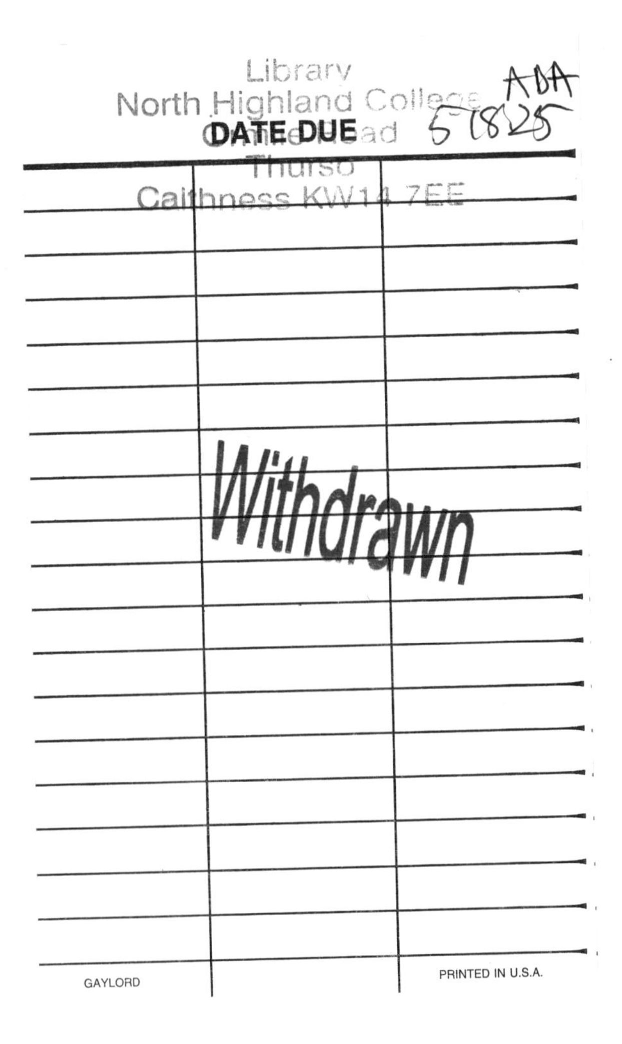
Library
North Highland College
Ormlie Road
Thurso
Caithness KW14 7EE
DATE DUE
ADA
5/8/25
Withdrawn
GAYLORD
PRINTED IN U.S.A.

Disclaimer

Whilst this publication has been carefully written and subjected to peer group review, it is the reader's responsibility to take all necessary steps to ensure that the assumptions and results from any finite element analyses which are made as a result of reading this document are correct. Neither NAFEMS nor the author can accept any liability for incorrect analyses.

How To Manage Finite Element Analysis in the Design Process

Author:

Vince Adams

IMPACT Engineering Solutions, Inc.

ISBN 1 874 376 12 3

ACKNOWLEDGEMENT

I wish to take this opportunity as Chairman of NAFEMS Education and Training Working Group, to thank the Working Group members for their help and support in the preparation of this book and, in particular, Derek Pashley who acted as Chief Reviewer. The composition of the Working Group is:

Adib Becker	University of Nottingham
Dave Ellis	IDAC
Trevor Hellen	Consultant
Bob Johnson	DAMT
Derek Pashley	Consultant
Anup Puri	BAe Systems
John Smart	North East Wales Institute, Wrexham
Bryan Spooner	Consultant
Jim Wood	University of Strathclyde

John Smart
Chairman, Education & Training Working Group
etwg@nafems.org

Contents

1. Introduction

By now, most engineering companies have acknowledged that product simulation in one form or another provides benefits in regard to correction of failure, robustness of design, cost of product or process, and product insight. Although many companies have realized some or all of these benefits, individual companies have experienced an uneven spectrum of them. Some research may make it apparent that the perceived benefits accorded to some companies are only a fraction of those anticipated. In a survey carried out in 2001, with results discussed at the NAFEMS World Congress in Lake Como, Italy, that year, it was apparent that many companies a have limited understanding of the possibilities for implementing simulation in the design process.[10] In the ensuing years, this has not changed dramatically.

1.1 Finite Element Analysis in Product Design

It is now widely understood that product simulation, and Finite Element Analysis (FEA) in particular, is a tool for use during the design process, rather than a tool for use in checking the suitability of a near-final design. There is, however, a growing concern that users with sub-par skills and/or engineering know-how are now armed with a tool that could either lengthen the design process by facilitating erroneous design decisions or, what is worse, lead a manufacturer to commit to products that are less optimized or less safe than anticipated. Software vendors are doing their jobs by adding more functionality in increasingly user-friendly interfaces with better, albeit varied, Computer-Aided Design (CAD) integration.

In the face of this dramatic rise in functionality, managers at many companies are finding themselves with the opportunity to use simulation for advanced analysis, but with less and less grasp of its capabilities and limitations. The engineering content—the purpose of the simulation task in the first place—is often overshadowed by the glut of information pouring out of these faster, "more intuitive" systems. The NAFEMS booklet *Management of FEA: Guidelines to Best Practice*[1] reminds us that impressive FE models buy a user very little if the meaning of the data is unclear or the task does not lead to improved design. **Oftentimes, very simple models, bearing little resemblance to the final CAD model, can provide more insight in a shorter period of time than can a more complex and highly detailed solution.** Less qualified users performing more complex analyses may cause a regression, rather than an improvement, in effectiveness.

What differentiates a company that gets maximum benefit from product simulation from one that does not? How can a manager know where his team stands in utilization effectiveness? Amazingly, while the short answer to this is simple, the implementation of that answer is complex— thus justifying the rest of this book and the time needed to read it. This booklet seeks to explain issues that may arise from introducing FEA into the design process, how they might turn into bad—if not dangerous— "best practices," and how these issues might be resolved.

This is a guide to managing FEA technology, not an introduction to the technology itself. This statement alone begs the question: Does this technology require management, or, like other engineering tools, does it sit in the product engineer's toolbox alongside the dial caliper and spreadsheet, with a similar lack of appreciation? The next few chapters make the case for an active management role in the challenging task of product simulation. With "mainstream analysis" growing in popularity, the complexities of the technology now require active management, unlike in the past when it was used in a more limited fashion. After making the case for active management, this booklet covers various aspects of simulation implementation and reviews means to control and optimize the effectiveness of each of these aspects. The final chapters discuss and summarize philosophy of management in an era when computer simulation of product performance is increasingly the norm versus the exception. The changing role of engineering management in a world of rapid product development may be beyond the scope of this book, but at a minimum the reader will be left with food for thought.

1.2 Target Audience

This book is not intended to justify the purchase of FEA software or convince anyone that it should be considered. The target audience of this book is the array of managers and team leaders who have already made an investment in analysis, or at least the decision to invest in it. This explanation is intended to help them focus their resources more effectively. Every company is in a different phase of implementing simulation, so some of the concepts and recommendations provided here may be moot. However, taken as a whole the information presented in this book may confirm a company's chosen path as either correct or warranting only minor adjustments. Admittedly, managers who are looking for direction in implementing FEA will get more out of this text than managers of established analytical teams, but readers are cautioned to keep an open mind regarding the efficiency of their own processes. There are many stories of managers who over-estimated their successes. In the words of Thomas Jefferson, "He who knows best knows how little he knows."

Both the author and NAFEMS are committed to helping the manufacturing and product development community utilize these important technologies more effectively. Should any reader have refinements or war-stories to offer, his or her input is welcome via the NAFEMS Education and Training Working Group (etwg@nafems.org) or the website (www.nafems.org.). Product simulation is a dynamic and growing industry through which many are still feeling the way. By working together—one of the greatest benefits of NAFEMS involvement—users can reach optimum solutions more quickly.

2. Product Development Challenges: Where Does FE Fit?

The product development process has been undergoing significant changes over the past decade, and the trend may be accelerating instead of leveling off. A few years ago, most companies were still struggling with effectively implementing Product Data Management (PDM) to forge some control over the massive quantities of revision and configuration data that CAD systems generate so easily and quickly. Product Lifecycle Management (PLM) had not yet made it into the acronym lexicon, but its core concepts were already looming. Now engineering organizations are trying to capture every aspect of the product development process in more complex data retention and recovery systems. It would seem that the natural course of events for all engineering processes is to include more detail, more quickly and to blur the differentiation between the various roles in product development.

For example, several FE vendors at the 2003 NAFEMS World Congress in Orlando, Florida, were sharing case studies of companies that had automated the engineering process of various components and systems to such a degree that sales engineers could enter product specifications into a computerized form, and the parts would almost design themselves. This was not smoke and mirrors, and these were not young upstarts in the industry. The power of such systems seems self-evident. However, at a roundtable discussion at the close of the conference few companies could envision the use of this level of automation because the targets for performance and form change frequently, and even fewer companies could justify the investment in time and money required for training before considering a solution of this nature.

2.1 A Typical Product Development Scenario

For the foreseeable future most companies will be designing and analyzing parts as they are needed, with little or no automation and much replication of effort. However, the tendency toward increased detail and complexity is still prevalent. Many users and managers alike operate under the misconception that increased analysis effectiveness stems from a tool's ability to analyze a completely, or almost completely, designed and modeled part, thereby validating its performance. This is the realm of the "mainstream analysis" products that have become commonplace in many design organizations. A common misconception is that if an analysis of a simplified model provides some benefit, an analysis of a part or system with every possible feature included must provide more benefit. The belief that all detail should be captured as early as possible in the design cycle justifies this. While a case can be made in certain circumstances to perform the first analysis on a part whose CAD model is nearly complete with all required features, these opportunities are few and far between. To address this misconception, the actual role of simulation in the design process should be explored.

In the traditional design process, still dominant for most parts and most companies, engineers or designers take a "best guess" at initial geometry based on several factors:

- Styling
- Fit with mating parts
- Historical geometry
- Known failure modes of previously tested, similar parts
- Required or anticipated manufacturing methods

With the push to capture as much detail as possible as early as possible, a 3D Solids CAD model is created, based on these factors, that very closely resembles a manufacturable part or system. From this "foundation," the acceptability of the part or system is explored. When a CAD model reaches this stage, it has usually established itself, psychologically and/or emotionally in the designer's eyes, as "The Part." This is called "Emotional Commitment."[2] It is a very important stage for a part because it has achieved a state in which it is assumed to be viable, and subsequent modifications will be considered only after their need is proven: **innocent until proven guilty**. Fortunately—from a reliability standpoint, not a cost standpoint—designers tend to produce a workable foundation more often than not. The fact that most designers, going by "gut feel," at least get close on the first shot is one of the impediments to true design—or up-front—simulation.

When an engineering organization is dominated by the presumption that initial design decisions are correct, additional commitment to the first pass makes perfect sense. Grief over a design that does not survive validation is compounded by multiple commitments made to a part or product direction before that validation occurs. Even when failures are observed, the typical assumption is that the basic premise of the design is sound and that minor changes—a rib here, a fillet there, a material swap—should fix the problem. Oftentimes, these are the only changes open to the team at this stage because the design already has passed on to the second stage of design commitment, "Concurrent Commitment."

Since most parts or sub-assemblies must interact with other parts or sub-assemblies, in the mid to later stages of the development cycle other engineers or teams, working concurrently with the resources in question, are counting on a certain bolt pattern, envelope size, or orientation. In many cases, therefore, the development team's hands are tied regarding the changes that can be considered to fix a problem found during the validation process. Similarly, as confidence in the starting point grows geometrically, tooling or sourcing may be started prior to validation.

This product development methodology can be considered a Decide-Commit-Validate (DCV) approach in that most, if not all, design decisions are accepted and implemented before the collection of decisions that comprises the final design is finally validated. A graphic depiction of this approach is shown in Figure 2-1.

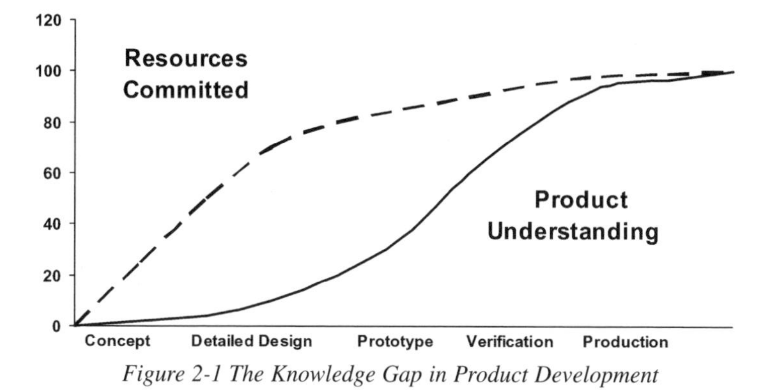

Figure 2-1 The Knowledge Gap in Product Development

The dashed line represents the resources committed to the development of a part or product as a percentage of all the resources to be committed, while the solid line represents the actual knowledge or understanding of how the design—the culmination of these resources and all the decisions made to that point—will perform. The curves represent the percentage of complete product performance knowledge at various stages of the product development cycle. The greater the gap between product understanding and resources committed, the greater the risk to the development organization that a negative variance between actual and anticipated performance will cause unnecessary delays and expenditures. In a DCV approach, a mistake made early in the product development stage can greatly impact the overall cost and release schedule of a product. This is analogous to walking into a casino and betting one's life savings on black.

Why is this acceptable in an established organization that most likely has checks and balances on every other type of expenditure or financial risk in its operations? The best answer to this question is that it is tradition, common practice, or inertia. Risk has always been associated with new product development and innovation. That is the purpose for the chunk of time at the end of the project schedule called "rework" or "redesign." One explanation for this common situation is suggested by Preston G. Smith and Donald G. Reinertsen in their book *Developing Products in Half the Time*[3]. The authors relate the Design in Process (DIP) to product or material inventory in the plant. Essentially, all development related functions, tasks, and expenditures, both in samples or salaries, are investments that have yet to reap a financial return. With a push in most companies for Just-in-Time (JIT) manufacturing principles, allowing DIP to accumulate without assurances as to its future value is a dangerous contradiction. It is, however, common practice in most companies.

Where does FEA fit into this product development scenario? In product development organizations that rely on detailed starting point geometry—a DCV approach—simulation is typically used after most or all initial design decisions have been made. Validation of a completed design using computer simulation is typically less costly than validation using physical prototypes. In a narrow view, a case could be made to justify FEA simply on this basis alone. In fact, design validation is often considered to be up-front analysis since it precedes a commitment (sometimes) in tooling.

With a general focus on analysis in the design process, this book does not dwell on the use of FEA for failure verification and resolution. This is not to downplay the significant role the technology has in this arena; it is huge. However, the better a product development group becomes at predictive simulation, the less it needs to rely on simulation to resolve product failures.

2.2 Predictive Simulation as a Competitive Advantage

Over the past decade there has been much hype and press regarding up-front or predictive analysis. The fact that this message has not changed radically in that period says something about the use of this technology. Intuitively, if everyone were on the same page with predictive analysis, the movers and shakers of the industry would be pushing us to the next level. Predictive analysis involves more than just the process of validating design before implementing prototypes. To make the most out of its investment in simulation technologies, an engineering organization needs to find ways to leverage the tool to improve the process, not simply shave some dollars and days off the end of it. An analysis tool does not provide a company with a competitive advantage. While lacking simulation might be a tangible competitive *dis*advantage, the fact of the matter is that competitive companies all have analysis tools, in many cases the same ones.

So, if everyone uses the same tools, how can a company gain a competitive advantage? By using the tools better and smarter than the competition. Using FEA to validate a design completed just as in the pre-analysis days provides the same innovative leverage as writing on a word processor rather than a typewriter does for literary creativity. Although the overall process is faster and less expensive, the work product is essentially the same. Consider the graph shown in Figure 2-2.

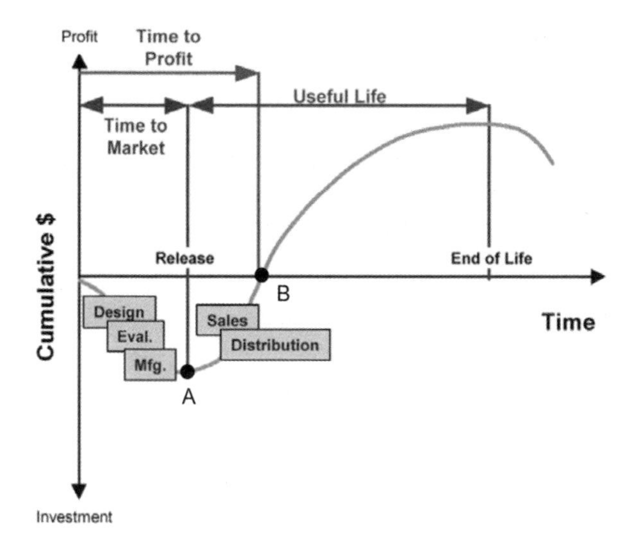

Figure 2-2 Product Development in Terms of Profitability

The vertical axis represents the net cost/profit of a product from its conception through the end of its useful life. The portion of the curve before Point A represents the DIP described above: the investment in product development. At the point the product is released to the market, the company starts to recoup its costs until such a time (Point B) when the return on investment becomes positive. Only at that point does the company make money from all the preceding work.

It is extremely important that both engineers and managers alike understand the relationship of DIP to profitability. It is this component of the profitability equation over which an engineering team has control. Two ways that the design team can impact profitability are to reduce (A) the development cost and/or (B) the development time. A study by McKinsey & Company as related in a subsequent study by Grant Thornton[4] found that profitability is enhanced much more by improvements to the latter than the former.

So how can FEA improve time to market beyond catching a faulty design before tooling is released? By addressing the root cause of the problem before it has propagated through the various design commitments described previously. An expert in the field of product development metrics was once asked what single metric would be the most telling indicator of process efficiency. His response was that it would be the measurement of how quickly mistakes were identified. In most cases, the design error that caused a product to fail validation occurred not just prior to the testing, but also in the initial decisions about sizing, materials, support features, fastening methods, or manufacturing methods. A faulty feature or concept is typically reviewed by many technical team members whose "gut feel" assessment is that it is probably OK.

2.3 Validation Before Commitment

An alternate approach to the DCV scenario described above is a DVC methodology: Decide-Validate-Commit. In this minor, yet important, adjustment to the traditional way of working, decisions are validated as they are conceived so that mistakes are caught as soon as possible in the process. This is essentially a cultural shift that may involve changes to the way CAD models are created, test data is accumulated, and analysis tasks are completed. To embrace this method is to fly in the face of the trend to capture as much detail as quickly as possible. Truly, less is more. Simplistic models that address initial sizing and feature placement precede detailed CAD modeling. Schematic structural models were commonplace before the advent of CAD as we know it today, especially in the aerospace industry. The value of this has not lessened with the ability to generate photo-realistic renderings in nearly real-time. In many cases, these geometries can be utilized as the basis for the final CAD models. When this is not possible, the process should not be cut short, as CAD is not *King*. A final CAD model is, in the end, simply the documentation of a set of design decisions. The product represented by this documentation is only as good as the design decisions it embodies.

In most cases, this subtle change to the design process will help to avoid significant cost and delay if the starting point geometry proves to be a problem. If the starting point design were acceptable, would this revised process provide any benefit? Problem avoidance is a difficult thing to use as justification for change, especially if the company has not been burned by repetitive hits from the same problem. An equally important benefit of the iterative Decide-Validate-Commit approach addresses the choices made in the initial part design that will have a profound effect on the total product cost and quality.

2.4 Simulation to Drive Innovation

Consider the piston shown in Figure 2-3. The normal design process for this part is to complete the initial design in CAD, with all the detail required for final documentation and manufacturing. Should the initial analysis in the DCV approach, utilizing the fully detailed CAD model, suggest that the design is acceptable, very little else would be done on this part. With the baggage of the complex CAD model, even suggestions for optimization seen in the validation are considered in light of the time required to make those modifications. In the DVC approach, however, the base features are straightforward and robust enough to be subjected to a quick sensitivity study. Should such a study suggest a weight and/or cost reduction that would not adversely affect the performance of the part, it could easily be incorporated. Even a rough feature optimization study could be performed without significantly affecting the turn-around time of the validation task.

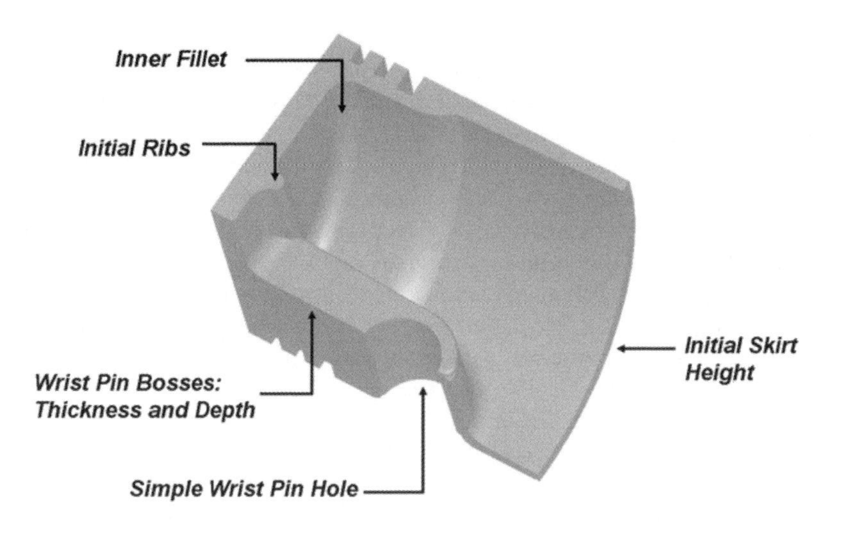

Figure 2-3 Features Required to Validate Piston Concept

The opportunity for cost optimization is greatest at the early stages of either the part or system design. Trying to backtrack once a design is nearly complete and committed is extremely difficult, even with FE tools. At the conceptual stage, however, the potential for optimization and exploration of options is nearly limitless. This is a benefit of the DVC approach that, while still intangible, is very strong. As companies are driven to more rapid innovation and stringent cost control, this presents a true engineering process change that can drive competitiveness and quality while keeping the costs related to initial design decisions to a minimum. Unfortunately, the functionality required to use conceptual or idealized geometry at the early stages of design where innovation can best be addressed has not been supported widely by the major CAD vendors. Because so many CAD-centric design organizations allow their processes to be guided by CAD functionality, as yet too few companies have embraced this intuitive approach.

2.5 Chapter Summary

Up-front analysis is defined here as analysis made before a decision is committed, preferably immediately following its conception. This shift in thinking can drive innovation and change. However, embracing a Decide-Validate-Commit approach involves enabling decision makers, typically design engineers, not only with tools but also with incentive. This means management must commit to the change. After reviewing the engineering process at a company that designs and manufactures plastic products with significant structural requirements in a market of rising plastic resin prices, it was suggested that the company would benefit if someone was assigned to focus on simulation at the conceptual stages of product development. The response was that while such a focus might be helpful in the future, right now they really just needed bodies designing products. This disconnect with present reality represents the challenge managers must face when looking for new ways to innovate. While a hard justification for a DVC simulation-driven process would be helpful, a critical examination of the true costs of "designing in the dark" may be the best way to justify the process change. In short, companies cannot continue to remain competitive by rolling the dice on new concepts or always making the safe moves. Gaining or maintaining a competitive position involves utilizing today's technologies to their fullest extent.

The following chapters discuss the challenges this shift brings with it and reviews suggestions for streamlining the process. While many of the discussions that follow are valid in a DCV focused design process as well, they have greatly reduced impact. Recall that engineers are seldom charged with performing an analysis; they are normally charged with solving a problem. Therefore, any tool or process that can bring early focus on the solution to a problem will make the chances of success, or at least the benefit from eventual success, greater.

3. What is FEA? What are its Capabilities and Limitations?

It is likely that any engineering manager who has approved the purchase of FEA tools for his or her team or approves the continued use of these tools knows of the basic terms and concepts related to it. However, before continuing with detailed discussions on the various aspects of FEA in the design process, a review of these concepts will ensure that all readers share a common understanding. If some of the terms in chapter 2 were not clear, this chapter should clarify them.

3.1 Basic FEA Concepts

Commercial finite element software has its roots in the 1950s aerospace industry. Prior to the early FEA tools, complex frame structures and continua needed to be defined with differential equations that quickly became too difficult to solve. By the early 1900s, research from Castigliano, Rayleigh, and Ritz had led to a method for predicting responses such as displacement by assuming potential shapes, defined by equations known as *shape functions*, of simple loaded systems and solving for a response by energy minimization. Work done by mathematician Richard Courant (1888–1972) around 1950 made this practical for structures that could not be solved easily with differential equations. He proposed linking many of these simple shapes, lines, or triangular areas and computing the total response of the system by combining the functions into a matrix format and solving them algebraically. As computers and matrix solving algorithms increased in power over the next decade, FEA found its place in industries that had critical safety issues and high manufacturing costs.

Today's FEA systems bear little resemblance to the 1950s codes on the outside, but the mathematical origins described above are still at their foundation. At their very essence, all FEA tools require a user to define a *mesh* consisting of *nodes* and *elements*. This mesh represents the system being studied, including any parts required to ensure that the parts of interest behave as intended. While full-featured FEA programs allow a user to create a mesh manually, most analysts utilize some level of automatic meshing using CAD data. Whether created manually or automatically at the solver level, the final mesh represents the only *geometry* the calculations will consider. This is an important point when CAD solids are relied on heavily as the starting point for analysis.

Wherever modeled parts interact with parts or environmental conditions that do not or cannot exist, the user needs to specify a reasonable replacement for that interaction. These "replacements," typically some combination of loads and constraints, are called *boundary conditions* since they represent the conditions at the boundary of what was modeled. Since the mesh represents physical parts, the mesh must be assigned *material properties* that provide the mathematical FE model with enough information about the material to satisfy the behavior being studied. Additionally, many finite element codes allow a user to simplify or idealize a three-dimensional part or feature and reduce it to a surface (2D) or a wireframe (1D) mesh representation. When these simplifications are employed, the user must input the information removed from the mesh with *element properties*. For example, in plates and shells the structure becomes a meshed surface with the element property "thickness."

Finally, the user must choose the physical phenomena to be captured by the model. The most common choice at this stage is to assume the physics are linear and static. While "common" doesn't always mean "right," many more complex behaviors can be reduced to linear statics if the user is trained to understand what has been lost by this approximation. More complex phenomena such as material plasticity and cyclic or transient dynamics can be captured by more experienced users.

3.2 Assumptions in FEA

As if all these choices were not enough, making them gets a user only to the point of initiating a solution. Once the solution is complete, the user must correctly interpret the results and make a decision as to their meaning with respect to the anticipated failure modes or allowable responses. Interpret?! One might think that with all the time put into building complex CAD solids and all the money spent on the latest and most popular FEA tools, one could expect immediately usable and accurate answers. Unfortunately, this is an unreasonable expectation.

While the CAD model may represent the design intent, there inevitably will be variations in the actual manufactured part above and beyond the tolerances allowed for in the inspection print. While the material properties chosen might be well documented in the most reliable sources, most materials have significant scatter even in their linear elastic properties due to a variety of processing or environmental factors. The variation in failure properties can be even greater. The eventual conclusion from this line of thinking is that most, if not all, inputs to a finite element model are assumptions, not knowns. With any assumption comes error or, at best, uncertainty. It is in the qualification and quantification of this uncertainty that the value of a simulation can be determined.

The tasks described earlier can be grouped into five categories for a typical analysis project:

- Geometry
- Mesh
- Properties
- Interactions
- Physics

The validity of the solution is dependent upon the validity of these assumptions. If a user does not understand the sensitivity of the results of interest to variations in any of these assumptions, it is likely that an erroneous interpretation of the results and subsequent erroneous design decision will be made. An understanding of the real meaning and limitations of each of these assumptions is therefore critical to a manager who is hoping to use simulation results to improve innovation.

3.2.1 Geometry

The geometry for most analyses will come from a CAD system, usually a 3D solids CAD system. Just because it usually comes from CAD solids does not always mean it should. Guidelines for this determination are reviewed in more detail in Chapter 5. It is dangerous to assume that a more accurate CAD model guarantees a more accurate analysis. While the starting geometry must be representative of the system under study, too much detail in the CAD model often leads a user to put too much stock in the result, for several reasons.

First of all, if the CAD model already looks like the production part, it is most likely that the design has progressed into the commitment stage, and there is most likely a pre-conceived behavior that can influence subsequent model inputs.

Secondly, the realistic and believable appearance of results on a detailed CAD model often masks the unrealistic nature of other assumptions used in the model. Accurate CAD cannot make up for poorly understood properties or boundary conditions. Too often, new to intermediate users spend more time on the creation of CAD geometry than in understanding the loads, restraints, elastic, or failure properties. This is another reason why less is more.

Finally, with more details come more chances to create features that cause trouble for the mesher, automatic or manual. A finite element solver has no concept of geometry. To the mathematical processes behind the scenes, the mesh is the geometry. If the geometric "template" used by the mesher creates poorly sized or shaped elements, error can be introduced into the results. If these bad elements are near an area of interest, this error can affect the validity of design decisions based on those results.

3.2.2 Mesh

A misunderstanding common to many design analysts is that any mesh based on accurate seeming geometry is a good mesh. As described previously, the size and shape of elements, especially in areas of high stress gradients, can impact the accuracy of the solution. The applicability of a mesh to capture the results of interest is an assumption within the user's control and cannot be taken for granted.

The finite element practitioner is responsible for three primary characteristics of the mesh he or she uses. These are:

- Proper element type or idealization
- Proper representation of the intended geometry
- Sufficient number of nodes and elements where required, or convergence.

3.2.2.1 Idealization

The rules and guidelines for choosing the appropriate element type are beyond the scope of this book, but it is important for managers to know that there are options beyond a tetrahedral mesh in a CAD solid. Typical element types are shown in Figure *3-1*.

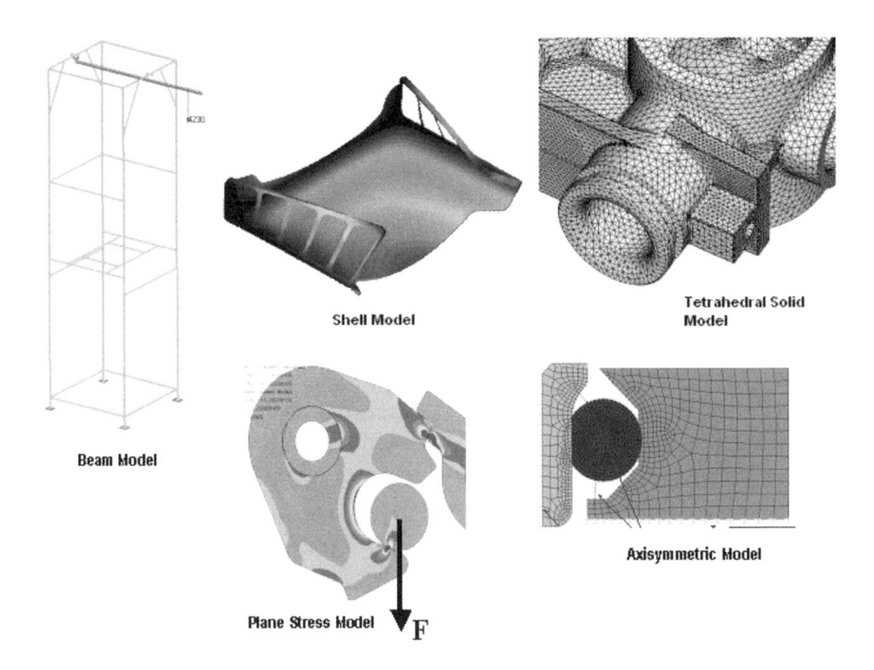

Figure 3-1 Idealizations Available in Most FEA Codes

A good rule of thumb for a first pass consideration of element type is to map the element type with the gross categorization of the geometry. If the system being studied is comprised of long slender components that might be solved with engineering beam calculations if the configuration were simpler, *Beam Elements* might be appropriate. If the part or system being studied is much greater in surface dimensions than thickness, then *Shell or Plate Elements* might be appropriate. If neither of these apply, than auto-meshed tetrahedrons might be the only choice. A manager may not need to make this call for FE users, but should be prepared to challenge them on their choices to ensure that the decision was based on consideration of the options instead of being a default choice for convenience...or worse.

3.2.2.2 Initial Geometric Representation

This may seem superfluous in the days of automeshed CAD solids, but the user is responsible for making sure the initial shape of the mesh captures the physical shape of the intended component within the scope of the approximation being made. This is primarily a concern for small features in a model. Chapter 5 discusses how any feature deemed important enough to be included in the system under study should have sufficient mesh resolution to capture its shape. When the mesh is too coarse at these features, and round holes start looking like square ones and fillets look like chamfers, results near these features will not be valid. If all the guidelines for feature inclusion, discussed later, are followed, a good check of the initial mesh is a shaded plot with the element edges not displayed. The shading should highlight the faceting of the mesh. Smooth surfaces should look smooth. Surface patterns that clearly indicate alternating normal directions may indicate an insufficient starting mesh.

3.2.2.3 Convergence

Convergence is the process of systematically increasing mesh density, either across the entire model or locally at areas of concern, until adding more nodes and elements does not change the results in the model by an amount the user deems acceptable. The addition of more mesh essentially serves the purpose of making the model more flexible, allowing it to better assume the proper shape at equilibrium or the correct strain field in areas of high gradients. Under-meshed or under-converged parts, such as those including too few elements thru the thickness of a thin walled solid, typically respond too stiffly in most cases, and the solution will under-predict deflections or stresses.

If the result of interest is plotted on the "Y" axis of a graph with the "X" axis reflecting the mesh density, as in Figure 3-2 [5], one can see that as the mesh density increases, the slope of the plot begins to approach zero. At that point the convergence error can be treated as zero.

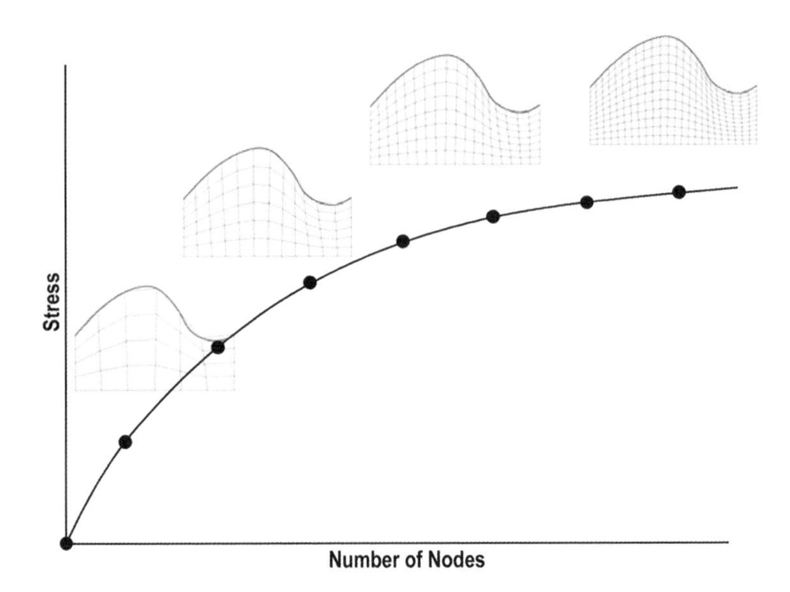

Figure 3-2 A Typical Convergence Plot

The amount of change determined as satisfactory is dependent upon the goals of the analysis and the validity of the other assumptions in the model. In a model where trends are being examined or first pass results are required to simply ensure performance characteristics are in line with initial expectations, a greater convergence tolerance or error is allowed. If a user is hoping to make critical decisions regarding failure, a more precise mesh with tighter convergence tolerances may be required.

Figure 3-3 shows an example of how stress can rise significantly at a small feature with an increasing mesh density. It is not difficult to see a scenario in which the convergence process brings the stress in this area from acceptable to unacceptable.

One could argue that an aggressive convergence process takes care of all other mesh related concerns. Theoretically, if a user attempted to fill a thin-walled solid model with tetrahedrons and was able to explore the variation in results as he doubled and tripled the number of elements through a wall or in other small features, he or she could make a case for the validity of solids for that particular problem. Similarly, taken to the theoretical extreme, the smaller the elements become, the less likely it is that a good automesher can create distorted elements. Additionally, the effects of poorly shaped elements can be observed and corrected with convergence.

The down side to this, as any user who has aggressively pursued convergence knows, is that it can take a long time on a substantial model to mesh, solve, re-

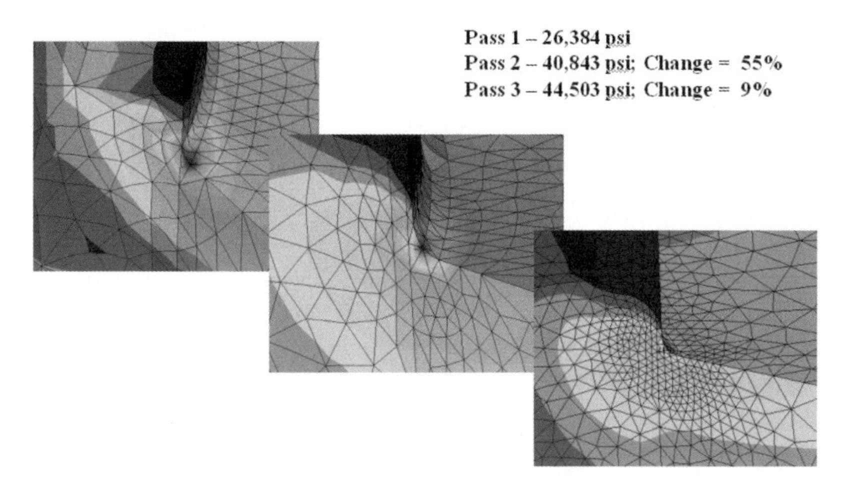

Figure 3-3 Example of Stress Convergence

mesh, solve, re-mesh, solve, etc. Getting the first mesh closer to the ideal mesh is a major timesaver. In the early days of FEA, with slower computers and solving algorithms, a characteristic of a "good" mesh was that it used the fewest nodes and elements to accurately represent the problem being studied. In today's world of desktop supercomputers, the definition of a good mesh must be: that which gets the user to the required answer the fastest. Often this may mean intentionally over-meshing the first pass so that convergence can be obtained in fewer iterations. However, whatever the approach to convergence, it must be considered and should be documented in the final project report.

Also remember that a mesh converged for one set of boundary conditions may not be converged for a different set. The response of a mesh to a unique set of loads and constraints is obviously unique. Therefore, it is reasonable to expect different areas of high stress gradients for different boundary conditions that must be converged independently.

3.2.3 Properties

As with the mesh assumption, there are multiple aspects of the properties assumption. The two primary categories are element properties and material properties.

Element properties are primarily tied to the choice of element used in the model, as addressed previously. FE codes require the inclusion of properties to make up for any physical dimension removed from the element. For solid elements, the geometry is 3D, and typically there are not any additional element property requirements. When a shell or plate element is used, the physical geometry of the element is like that of a CAD surface. The thickness must be accounted for with a property. Additionally, any thickness variation in the true 3D wall represented by this element, such as draft in a plastic part, must be accounted for or explained away, usually with a discussion on the validity of the constant wall thickness assumption. Removing one more dimension, beam elements are represented by lines, so the two physical dimensions that represent the cross-section must be entered as properties. As with the tapering wall, any physical variations from a constant cross-section must be dealt with using either additional properties or a discussion as to why a constant cross-section is valid for the study at hand. A discussion of element properties can be used to help analysts remember the level of idealization and approximation represented by their FE model and, thus, help them stay grounded.

The other property assumption, material properties, is clearly important to the validity of the solution, but, interestingly, glossed over by too many beginner or intermediate analysts. In pursuit of a valid linear static FE solution, typically only the elastic properties of a material are required to complete a study. However, the source or validity of this data is not always given proper scrutiny. For steels, determining input properties can be pretty straightforward. At the other end of the spectrum falls the category of materials generally known as *plastics*. While in most engineering applications, the elastic properties of steel remain constant across alloys, strain rates, time, and modest temperatures ranges, the exact opposite can be said about plastics. An analyst charged with predicting behavior of plastic parts must not only understand the complexities of FEA, but also the incredible variation of properties, even within the same base polymer. Once again, the manager of a design team using FEA to predict plastic part performance does not need to understand all of the implications of strain rate sensitivity or glass orientation on properties, but he or she should be able to challenge the decisions made by his or her staff.

Assuming the proper elastic properties of a material are chosen with a good understanding regarding the sensitivity of the results of interest to those properties, the user still needs to know what to do with the data, as stated earlier in this text. This implies knowledge of the failure mechanisms and associated failure properties of the material and allowables that might be specific to the application. While the fatigue strength of a material does not affect the results of the FE solution, it does make a big difference when those results are interpreted. These failure properties can vary greatly, even for steels, so the user should also demonstrate that as much, if not more, care went into proper selection of allowables.

3.2.4 Interactions

As stated previously, the interactions between what was modeled and what was not modeled are represented with Boundary Conditions (BCs). While there is some disagreement between various FE references on this, both restraints and loads (often referred to as *natural boundary conditions*) are categorized as Boundary Conditions to generalize the conditions at the models extents or boundaries. To that end, the BCs should not cause the model to move in a manner inconsistent with actual physical interaction, nor should they prevent movement the actual physical parts allow, nor should they impart stiffness that the actual physical parts do not have. Helping a design team keep these conditions in mind and evaluating BC choices by these simple guidelines can prevent reams of bad analyses from delaying product release.

In many cases, a cursory review of the interactions does not suggest a clear BC choice. In these cases, it is imperative that the analyst explore the various suggested options to determine how sensitive the results of interest are to this assumption and thereby provide a scientific basis for the eventual choice, avoiding "gut feel." A good discipline for all users is to explore more than one BC option for a given interaction and justify why the one chosen is appropriate. Mistakenly applying "obvious" boundary conditions may be the biggest cause of FEA failure in design analysts.

3.2.4.1 Boundary Conditions and Model Extent

How does a user know where to put the loads and restraints if they are that important? It seems as if it would be much more straightforward to just model the inter-connecting parts. While this approach sounds reasonable, keep in mind that an important element of modeling is simplistic approximation of the world beyond the part of interest or a small assembly of parts. Realistically, one needs to stop modeling somewhere, otherwise finite element analysis would be limited to modeling things that had very few to no interactions.

With today's software and improved assembly modeling and calculation of contact behavior, the option to include more components when their interactions are not clear is more of an option than it used to be. Users should understand the assembly modeling capabilities of the tool so that they can exploit this important improvement in the technology.

Even with the improved ability to add in ancillary parts to get a better estimation of what is happening to the parts of interest, representing boundary interactions is still a critical skill for all users. The rules and guidelines for boundary conditions are beyond the scope of this book. It is most important to know that simplified approximations of interactions must represent actual interactions on the parts of concern, and that invalid choices often generate results that look like valid choices. Users should not take BC construction for granted.

3.2.5 Physics

Finally, the majority of analyses performed today are still linear and static. A manager must help his team remember that these are just as important assumptions as the other four. Just because they are easy, fast, common, default, or whatever does not mean they are always applicable. NAFEMS has some excellent documentation on nonlinear and dynamic analyses that can help managers and their design teams identify the limitations of these assumptions. Suffice it to say that an invalid linear assumption often places results on the wrong side of the Go-No Go line, leading to costly ramifications when physical validation commences.

3.3 Chapter Summary

FEA is a very complex, yet tried and true process that many software companies, in their most recent releases, have managed to make seem simple. If the reader learns nothing else from this chapter, it must be that the use of this technology is anything but simple. FEA is an engineering tool, no more, no less. As with any tool, its effective use requires adequate knowledge of how it works. A manager is charged with ensuring that his or her team comes to the best design decisions as quickly as possible, so knowledge of how the tools work is important if the process is to be kept on track. All readers are encouraged to dig deeper than this extremely superficial and simplistic review of the technology, and a review of the NAFEMS introductory texts[11] is a great place to start.

All users, regardless of years of experience or academic degree, will take short-cuts with the construction of the inputs or the assumption set used in an analysis. Running with the first BC option that comes to mind, using input or failure material properties provided in the FE software's built-in database, and basing conclusions on the results of an initial mesh are very common practices. It is likely that this lack of diligence will not result in catastrophic design decisions because few companies base their final critical decisions solely on FEA results. Many users still employ FEA for trend studies that neutralize uncertainty by comparing changes in runs that all have the same errors built in. It is important to remember that when a design team starts to integrate FEA more into the decision making process and allows it to drive innovation, the penalty for improper care in developing assumptions becomes more critical. Additionally, while every bad FE assumption does not necessarily result in a design crisis, many do. Is this a reasonable risk when a more thoughtful and meaningful analysis process requires only a little more effort?

4. Implementing FEA in the Design Process

Having a working knowledge of FE technology, reputable software, and bright and enthusiastic users is the easy part of implementing FEA into the design process. When one considers that competitors in many industries have access to the same software, resources, and talent, it becomes apparent that gaining a competitive advantage with advanced simulation requires more than a surface level commitment. To reach leadership positions in their industries, many companies are realizing that the process by which innovation is achieved is as important, if not more important, than the underlying product technologies. Most product innovations are not based on proprietary or revolutionary breakthroughs in materials or electronics, but on novel and creative utilization of existing technologies. One could even make the case that a company's process is their real competitive differentiator, and successful products are really only a by-product of that process.

Consequently, it follows that to truly make advanced simulation technologies an innovation driver, a company must complement a successful process or help re-engineer a stagnant one. Either way, the integration of simulation should be deliberate, with a conscious plan to reduce costs and improve development schedules or product quality. Companies that have truly made simulation an integral part of the design process have several common characteristics in three areas:

(1) constant ***evaluation*** and re-evaluation of the process,
(2) well thought out ***implementation*** plan stating the expected benefits and goals, and
(3) documented means to ***validate the results*** and the business benefits/measured goals.

A clarification of terms is warranted at this point. For the purposes of this book, *verification* refers to the process ensuring that the finite element or other mathematical model satisfies the intention of the model or provides the best answer for the given set of inputs. *Validation*, on the other hand, refers to the process of correlating the simulation output against intended real-world performance. Another way to look at it is that verification checks the accuracy of the simulation, while validation checks the appropriateness of the simulation to the engineering challenges being addressed.

4.1 Evaluation

The integration process must begin with a comprehensive evaluation of these inter-related areas:

1. corporate needs, both economic and technological,
2. people and computing resources, and
3. current simulation industry offerings.

Evaluation of economic needs should begin with a review of the possible business benefits of simulation. Focus the evaluation on areas of the product design process where the greatest impact can be achieved most quickly. A highly visible product line or component family should be chosen, and the business benefit expected should be clarified. Questions such as these should be asked:

> Is the goal to reduce development time or cost?
> Will the greatest impact come from cutting material costs?
> Will market share increase if we develop safer products or improve quality?
> Can profitability or time-to-market improve by reducing testing needs?

Identification of the business benefit keeps other decisions in focus.

The technological portion of the needs analysis determines the analysis types required to adequately model a company's parts or systems. Understanding the requirements and limitations of each type of solution or modeling type is critical when evaluating tools and the engineers' ability to use them.

Following the needs analysis, the evaluation should focus on the human resources required to make the integration successful. First and foremost is the correct choice of users. Enthusiasm is a critical characteristic for a new analyst to have. Chosen individuals should be excited about the technology and willing to devote time (usually personal) to learning the theory behind it and practical application techniques. Without this enthusiasm, growth will be slow or non-existent, and the analyst's effectiveness will be minimal. Additionally, this person should have a solid grounding in engineering fundamentals and the mechanics of materials, along with respectable engineering judgment. Under these conditions, the problem set-up, assumption set, and results interpretation will be sound. If a suitable candidate cannot be identified internally, the search for one should expand externally.

Another important resource to evaluate is the availability of time in the project schedule to insert an additional and sometimes lengthy task. As with CAD in the 1980s, it is fair to expect some delay and redundancy while the integration of simulation ramps up. The trick is to minimize the losses without neglecting the components that are needed to ensure success. Identify and map out time to properly install, train, execute, verify, and validate the simulation process.

When evaluating hardware resources, keep in mind that, while improving rapidly, FEA is still very resource intensive. Tremendous gains in efficiency can be realized by supplying sufficient computing power to users. If the task of simulation is perceived initially as too lengthy, or if it is too difficult to get real problems to run on existing hardware, it may never achieve its expected goals. Computing needs vary considerably with respect to solution type, software choice, and product needs.

CAD compatibility, a seamless interaction with CAD geometry, is important. However, the analysis functionality buried into various CAD interfaces as currently offered has the potential to be limiting. The benefits of CAD compatibility vary with the type of solution required. Solid "potato-shaped" parts that can be automatically meshed benefit the most from a tight link with CAD. Parts or systems that are primarily beams and plates benefit the least. When looking at CAD-embedded tools, one key consideration is the portability of both training and data should the CAD system be replaced. An open interface that can read multiple CAD formats, model all element types, and read and write multiple FEA formats may be a more appropriate choice if a company's simulation needs encompass various geometric regimes.

Additionally, it is important to evaluate a supplier's market-share, installed base, and reputation in the market. Place a strong emphasis on support and training. Few engineers have the time or patience to pore over manuals, and most will hit the wall quickly if hotline support does not provide the application specific help they need. Software developers must have credible expertise in the training and support of their systems as well as developed relationships with experts in the implementation and application of the technology; this ensures that a user's growth will be supported. Software developers must be genuinely interested in partnering with an organization to guarantee success, even if the purchase is small. These are important issues to new users. Ask suppliers to discuss or demonstrate how they will be supportive.

4.2 Implementation

Remember that after the initial evaluation, the evaluation process must continue throughout the life of the implementation, because the company's needs change, available resources change, and the simulation industry changes rapidly. If a company's needs, resources, and market have been evaluated properly, adjusting the internal processes to take advantage of simulation can be straightforward. The steps taken to implement the technology will play a key role in the company's flexibility downstream. The three components of a successful implementation are (1) the company's plan, (2) the training program, and (3) the choice of initial and on-going projects.

4.2.1 Develop a Plan

A documented plan for evaluation, implementation, verification, validation, and growth is critical. The plan need not be complex, but it should contain the following components:

Goals or business benefits of the technology: Set expectations, because without expectations, success cannot be evaluated.

Periodic re-evaluation: Do not leave anything to chance. Schedule a semi-formal review of the current implementation. Checking new releases of FEA software against proven benchmarks can help ensure the implementation stays on track. NAFEMS benchmarks can be helpful for this, as can test models that contain critical behaviors for simulating a product's performance.

Process for initiating an analysis or study: Define the optimal interaction between users and others who must work with the data. Define priorities and formats for inputs that will be exchanged.

Develop documentation procedures: Most companies have rigid guidelines for test results, but few have guidelines for analysis documentation.

Build time for validation into the plan: Failure to correlate analysis to test data and review methods may lead to inefficient studies, or worse, potentially disastrous inaccuracies.

On-going training and education: Basic software training is not sufficient. Advanced skills, as well as improved engineering knowledge such as structural mechanics, vibration, and material behavior, are important to prevent stagnation and the propagation of bad habits.

This plan should be documented and made available to all who use or interact with the technology. It should be a dynamic plan and open to challenge in the search for continuous process improvement.

A key focus of the implementation should be training—the technical growth of the users. User groups are excellent ways to interact with others and exchange knowledge. Many companies engage outside experts to provide coaching or mentoring to their users. Additionally, on-going software training should be mandatory. One experienced analyst suggested that, "Good users will readily admit they need to know more; those who feel satisfied are probably in trouble." Many users do not model, analyze, and interpret results efficiently, or even accurately. However, most of them do not realize their shortcomings unless a major mistake costs the company money. Do not wait. If the value of introducing the technology existed in the first place, the value of on-going training should be self-evident.

Management and/or corporate buy-in is crucial to growth of the program. If the initial project was chosen correctly, and the results were deemed successful, advertise these successes internally and promote the achievements. If the initial projects are judged unsuccessful, a widespread simulation program may never gain corporate acceptance. The correct choice of an initial project is key.

4.3 Validation

The lack of validation and correlation can cause simulation to remain a small part of the overall design process at most companies. The validation process should address both the economic and technological goals set in the initial needs evaluation.

Key to the economic validation process is confirmation of expected business benefits. When these expectations are met or exceeded, it is easy to justify growing the program. A solid understanding of the business benefits is also important when validating the return on an investment. Typically, the price tag of analysis resources is higher than CAD and requires more justification.

Validating the technical accuracy of the results should be more straightforward than validating the economics. Correlation is a goal all analysts strive for. However, dead-on accuracy and correlation may not be as important as qualifying the results. This basically means quantifying the error and uncertainty introduced as a result of modeling and boundary condition assumptions. In many situations, loads, geometry, and properties are not well understood, and the stress or strain in an actual test unit cannot be measured. In these cases, accuracy becomes academic and the quality or applicability of results becomes the important measure of success. Additionally, one must remember that physical measurements are subject to error. Test fixturing is inconsistent; prototypes are not always assembled as expected; and most means of measuring stresses, strains, and/or deflections are fraught with error. With all the potential for differences between test and analysis results, much luck is involved when the data are closely matched.

The needs of the design analyst are different from those of the traditional analyst. To keep project cycles on track, design analysts frequently need to make product decisions quickly based on incomplete data. Consequently, sound engineering judgment plays a key role in interpreting and qualifying test, field, inspection, and QA data. Simulation data falls into the same category. To be able to qualify analysis data accurately and quickly, the following steps should be used before, during, and after the simulation.

4.3.1 Validation Guidelines

The following guidelines should help put analysis in its proper perspective:

Develop an understanding of the full system, including design tolerances, manufacturing tolerances, and assembly methods. Hand calculations should be used to quantify rough expectations of stress and displacement. If historical product data or previous analyses are available, they should be reviewed to form expectations of performance. To debug the assumptions, a design review with all the players in the design and manufacturing process is recommended. It does not take an analyst to suggest that there may be variability in properties or assembly methods. While this step exposes the analyst to criticism, it is the best way to grow and the only way to ensure that all possible scenarios are accounted for in the simulation. This also helps promote that crucial corporate buy-in.

Perform a sanity check on methods and assumptions after the analysis. If possible, reconvene the design review team mentioned previously to discuss the results in terms of assumptions and expectations. Use common sense. If the results do not match the expectations, users must discipline themselves to resolve these discrepancies. The team may learn that long held assumptions about system behavior were not correct and that the simulation enlightened all to the actual situation. At this stage, the experience of an expert—internal if available, external if needed—should be engaged to bulletproof the methods used and results calculated.

Assemble a testing program for assumption validation and data correlation to be performed or observed by the analyst. Keeping the analysis and testing functions linked minimizes errors in communication and unnecessary assumptions. Assumptions or variables should be isolated using test or prove-out models. These should be simple configurations that are easy to reproduce in testing. A good rule is "Test what you analyze; analyze what you test." Any differences between test results, analysis results, and actual field test data should be resolved.

Document assumptions, methods, results, and validation steps. Develop documentation so that an outsider to the project can quickly qualify the assumptions and results of the simulation and determine the applicability to his or her needs. After the only analysis user quit at one company, the management had serious doubts about continuing their simulation program because, since the user was never required to document his methods, assumptions, or results in a cohesive format, they could not validate that they had ever achieved any business benefit. Build documentation into the implementation plan, standardize it, and utilize it to summarize the data and reinforce the validation process.

4.4 Chapter Summary

Simulation technology has been proven to save time and money many times over. However, proper integration of simulation into the design process takes planning and requires a change in the way projects are structured. Set goals in terms of the business benefits desired. Keep these in mind throughout the evaluation, implementation, and validation stages, and let them guide decisions. Take the time to understand individual needs and the limitations of the tools available. Develop a plan and stick to it. Finally, validate both the business benefits of simulation and quality of the team's results. Adhering to these general guidelines and developing a strong implementation program will minimize the chances of error and maximize opportunity.

One of the most important points to learn from this chapter is that a full engineering understanding of the system being studied is critical to the success of a simulation or analysis. Choose to be skeptical, even cynical, about the results...and the capabilities of the analysis users in the organization. Simple models should be used to prove out assumptions and qualify data in terms of eventual goals. Only after some initial models and a thorough review of the overall process should users attempt to model complex assemblies or behavior. Users should not hesitate to ask for help and should be prepared to justify their assumptions and methods. Popular trends in the industry have served to downplay the importance of thoughtful modeling, multiple simulation options, and careful results interpretation. Companies entering into design simulation are best served by researching the technology and how it is used at cutting-edge corporations.

Above all else, be patient and encourage the use of common sense. Design engineers are trained to find solutions to tough problems, and the growing role of the design analyst is the logical progression of these skills. Analysis should be used with the same checks and balances as those employed for other tools.

5. Integrating CAD and FEA

Learning to balance CAD modeling against the needs of analysis is a difficult task facing users these days. There is no shortage of vendors offering that holy grail of design: push-button solutions at almost any stage of CAD modeling. For a certain class of problems and with the proper training in mechanics of materials, convergence, boundary conditions, and other fundamental skills, this type of tool can be very effective. Even within that class of problems—primarily parts that can and should be meshed with solid tetrahedrons—improper modeling techniques can render results useless. This chapter reviews several common situations and the role CAD geometry can play in the enhancement or complication of simulation.

5.1 Planning CAD for FEA

It is important to remember that CAD integration does not ensure success with FEA, nor does it imply it. In many cases, the existence of a CAD solid model can hinder success with simulation. There are two primary reasons for this.

1. A detailed CAD model may be too far along in the design process to allow anything more than design validation.

2. The desire to use the CAD model may preclude employment of the proper idealization.

As discussed in Chapter 2, simulation can support a new design methodology for improved innovation only if the information on design decisions can be gathered quickly. Ideally, this would happen simultaneously with the proposal of the concept, although very shortly after the proposal is still acceptable. This can happen only if CAD and simulation are properly coordinated.

Even if the CAD modeling is done with every intention of engaging analysis before any design locks are imposed, many companies find it hard to get beyond design validation due to roadblocks thrown up by available geometry. The following example illustrates this point perfectly:

At one engine manufacturer, a typical piston model, shown in Figure 5-1 and referenced earlier in Section 2.4, contained many features having little impact on structural or thermal performance that were required for proper operation of the part.

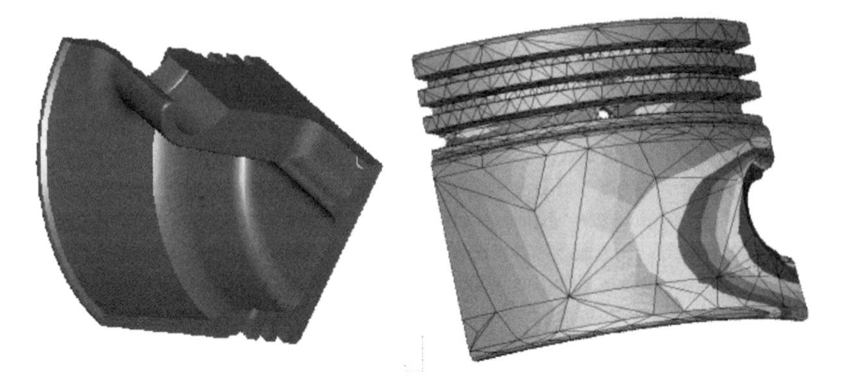

Figure 5-1 Piston Model with All Production Features

Oil passages, small fillets, chamfers on the ring grooves, lands, draft, and even the company logo were included in the CAD model before passing it onto analysis. The development of this CAD model took over a week. The analysts then removed or suppressed as many of these features as they could and proceeded with the validation. If the configuration passed...done! If not, it was sent back to design for the next best guess. If this sounds familiar, there is good reason.

In a comprehensive evaluation of their product design process, it was determined that only six features were required in the CAD model for piston concept validation. Analyzing the piston at this stage provided many benefits. First, the designer time invested before validation was performed was minimal. Second, the analyst spent no time on clean-up and less time on meshing and solving. The third and most subtle benefit was that the analyst could easily modify this simple model to optimize the design. The analyst could even utilize automated shape optimization tools with little fear of crashing the feature tree. This optimized piston could be passed back to the designer in less time than needed for the single validation process previously described.

5.2 Establishing CAD Model Requirements

The previous example highlights the importance of a clearly communicated goal and a focus on the minimum CAD model requirements at the planning stage of a project. In general, the CAD needs of the validation process are dependent upon several factors. These should be reviewed with the design team before starting any CAD or FEA tasks.

5.2.1 The Goal of the Project

The unknowns in a design problem should be detailed and documented and the appropriate means for resolving them determined. In some cases, physical testing may be the only choice. For those deemed resolvable with simulation, the approach to complete the analysis should include a discussion of what geometry support the simulation requires. There are many examples beyond the piston example that demonstrate the importance of this. In one project, a new plastic snap-fit design that had to withstand rigorous pull-put forces was required for a threaded fastener. Since the ID, OD, length, and material were established from previous programs of a similar nature, the snap geometry was the only question. 3D solids at the development stage would have been overkill, and all the dangers associated with complete-looking CAD models might have surfaced. To resolve this key portion of the design, various snap geometries were constructed as plane stress cross-sections in the FE pre-processor and iterated until an optimal design was reached. This was then communicated to the CAD designers who incorporated it into the final part. The majority of the part geometry was driven by these snap features, so any up-front CAD work would have been wasted. Clearly, identifying the goal and CAD requirements up-front helped speed this project along. The use of a plane stress idealization was also crucial to the rapid optimization of the feature, something that would have been very difficult in 3D solids.

5.2.2 The Idealization to be Used

It has been said that if the only tool available is a hammer, the whole world looks like a bed of nails. This is directly applicable to the front-ending of simulation with CAD solids. Once created, the natural tendency is to want to use them. On top of that, it is difficult in most pre-processors to do anything with a solid model other than automesh it with tetrahedrons. In fact, it is this "build a solid, get a tet mesh" paradigm that accounts for a large part of the development and marketing budget of many software vendors. Where appropriate, this method is very efficient, allowing users to get to the analysis with a minimal amount of effort. However, the simple fact remains that multiple element and modeling types were developed and maintained over the last 30 years because, in many cases, they are more appropriate.

Most thin walled structures are more accurately and efficiently modeled with shell elements; most long, thin components are better served by beam elements. It is in the transition between CAD solids and idealized models that current technology fails the believer in the CAD Master-Model. If the CAD model is not constructed with analysis in mind, extracting a mid-surface for shells can be painful. Without automated mid-surface extraction tools, the CAD solid becomes more of a hindrance than a help.

Switch the discussion to beam modeling, and the thin list of automated tools drops to an imperceptible amount. A finite element modeler that automatically extracts neutral axis models out of CAD solids has not yet been realized in the major pre-processing software.

Of course, one needs to understand that a beam idealization is required before one searches for tools to create it. Again, the existence of CAD solids and the pressure to use them has obscured this understanding. A case in point: one equipment manufacturer purchased a CAD-embedded, tet meshing, FE tool. While the lead engineer was knowledgeable about structures and a licensed professional engineer, he had no background in FEA, and since his only FE training was in this tool, he was not even aware of beam elements. Being limited to a CAD-embedded tetrahedral meshing tool, he was able to mesh and solve only one I-beam component in the more complex frame structure shown in Figure 5-2. In a verification study performed later with an outside resource, a more appropriate beam idealization showed a ten times greater displacement in the components of interest.

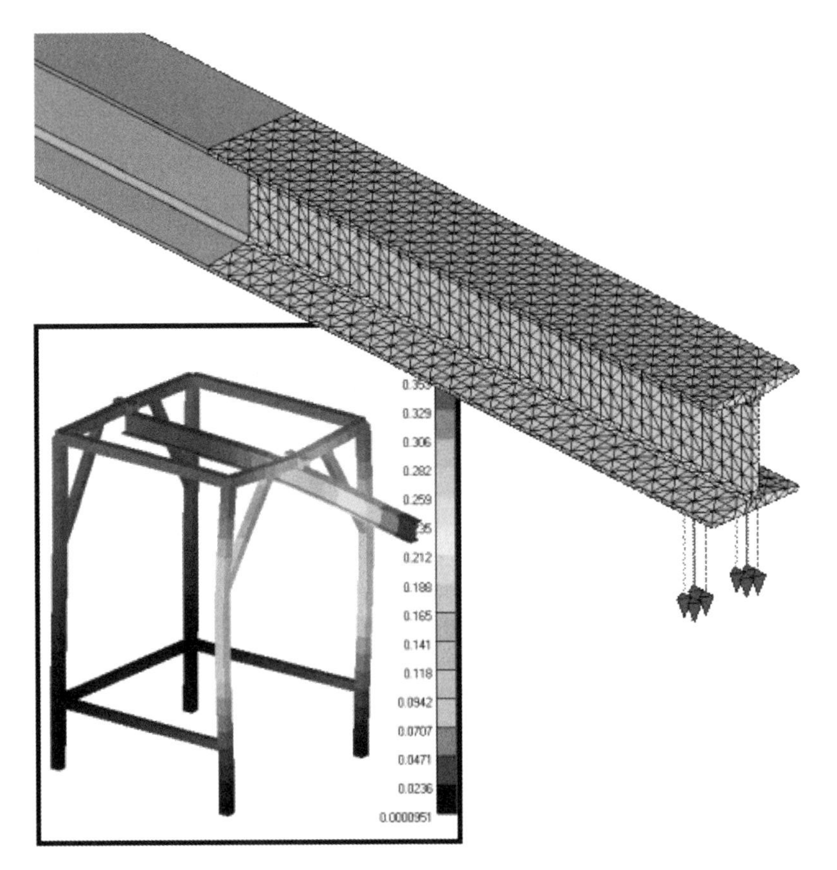

Figure 5-2 Structural Steel Frame

Good engineers can and will do bad FEA when improperly prepared. In this case, the engineer's choice of tools precluded his ability to solve this problem correctly, even if he had been aware of beam elements. However, there are many cases of users who have access to the appropriate idealization trying to force solid tets into a pre-existing CAD model. In one such case, a major snowplow manufacturer developed the bad habit of utilizing linear tetrahedrons in their large sheet metal parts. Most of these elements were highly distorted and never had more than one element through the thickness, a recipe for overly stiff results, as discussed in Section 3.2.2.3. This was done to leverage their existing CAD solids. Upon a detailed review of their processes, it became clear that this modeling mistake actually propagated a series of bad decisions regarding boundary conditions, static rather than dynamic analysis, and results interpretation so skewed that their years of analysis may have yielded very little useful data. Subsequently, they have made great strides in their analysis program by switching to shell elements and performing more dynamic analyses.

CAD techniques that enable a high level of integration and parameterization while still facilitating proper analysis techniques are discussed later in this chapter.

5.2.3 The Timeframe for Making Design Commitments

In today's world of accelerated development cycles, the common answer to the inevitable scheduling question of "When do you want it" is "We need it yesterday." This being impossible, prioritizing the unknowns in a project can help to determine the best starting point for a simulation, if this is the best means to resolve these unknowns. Some quick sizing calculations on primitive representations might suffice for extremely urgent decisions. The geometries for these might be created better in the analysis pre-processor. For decisions that warrant a more thorough evaluation, building minimal geometry in CAD should still follow the other guidelines described in this chapter.

5.2.4 The Use Of Existing Geometry

When a design decision involves parts that utilize existing, detailed CAD models, it must be determined if their geometry is acceptable in light of other factors described herein, and guidelines later in this chapter should be considered for any simplifications that might be warranted. If this is not the case, then more appropriate geometry should be planned.

5.2..5 The Type Of Analysis To Be Performed

The type of analysis (i.e. static, modal, thermal) has an impact on the level of detail required in the starting geometry. Again, knowledge of this minimal detail level can avoid costly waste in modeling time before a design is validated. If there is a question about the importance of certain details, test models can be used to quantify their impact, if time permits and the time saved over the total number of studies utilizing this information justifies it. If this cannot be justified, take the safe route, include the feature, and pay the run time penalty. Wrong answers obtained quickly are still wrong.

5.2.5.1 Thermal

A thermal analysis—one in which temperature is the primary output—requires a low level of detail, since most small fillets, chamfers, and other features have little impact on the results of interest. However, if the temperatures found are later to be used as input to a stress analysis, it might be convenient to use the same mesh for both analyses, since the temperature field over the part is usually represented as nodal values for both the thermal analysis output and the stress analysis input.

5.2.5.2 Modal / Displacement Only

Analyses that primarily calculate the stiffness and deformation of a structure typically require a low level of detail. Features that affect the stiffness and features in the load path must be included. However, small holes, fillets, and chamfers are usually inconsequential as to the end result.

5.2.5.3 Stress

A stress analysis typically requires the highest level of modeling detail. However, foreknowledge of the areas of concern can help minimize this. Also remember that including the detail in the CAD model is only part of the solution. If a small feature is deemed worthy of inclusion, then it is important to ensure mesh convergence at that feature so that the results are reliable. A small feature that is included, but not converged, is a waste of time and disk space. While this chapter focuses primarily on the creation of geometry for analysis, when existing geometry is simplified for an analysis, it provides the exception to the inclusion/convergence rule. In many cases, suppression or deletion of a feature is not possible or cost effective due to the complexity of a CAD model. In these cases, a coarse mesh at that feature may be warranted.

5.3 Solid Modeling and Dirty Geometry

When producing a solid model simply for the purpose of drawings, a certain degree of carelessness and sloppiness is tolerable, since small edges, discontinuities, and small surfaces never show up in the macro scale of most prints. However, as more companies strive to use the CAD model as a "master database" for all downstream activities such as CAM and FEA, designers need to take a second look at commonly accepted modeling practices. Manufacturing engineers charged with generating tool paths from CAD solids typically echo the same complaints regarding geometry as analysts do. These weaknesses can be clumped into two primary categories: (1) a fragile and cumbersome feature structure that precludes minor adjustments to the geometry and (2) sloppy or "dirty" geometry creation that produces those small features, mentioned above, that wreak havoc on tool path generators and meshers. For the purpose of analysis, if the prior discussions regarding the development of minimal geometry for concept validation are taken to heart, the problem of overly complex parametric feature dependencies can be left in the hands of CAD best practices, since this should happen after the simulation is complete. This section focuses on the concept of dirty geometry.

5.3.1 Why are Small Features an Issue?

To understand the importance of "clean" geometry to meshing, it makes sense to understand a little about the meshing process. Most automatic meshers subdivide the surface topology of a solid with respect to a nominal element size. This size is usually suggested by the mesher based on feature sizes in the model, but ultimately is under the control of the user. The mesher attempts to seed the surface edges with node spacing at this nominal size, or as close as it can get, rounding to the closest whole number. If an edge is smaller than this nominal element size, it specifies one element for that edge and moves on. Once the edges have been mapped, the mesher attempts to pave the surfaces with triangles having sides as close to the nominal size as possible. Most meshers utilize shape distortion rules as they determine if an element complies with software or user specified guidelines. Typically, these rules come into play when the size of an edge or surface forces one or more sides of the triangle to be much smaller than the nominal size, forcing a gross deviation from equilateral—the ideal shape. What a mesher does in these cases is software dependent. If a mesher tries to build an acceptable mesh in that area but cannot, some tools stop, and some continue with the best elements they can make. Some generate an error message, and some do not. Once the surfaces are mapped, the mesher fills the volume with tetrahedrons using similar shape distortion rules and similar workarounds when problems are found.

Recalling the discussion in previous chapters regarding the impact element distortion has on local element stiffness, it should be clear that the results near distorted elements are suspect, if not grossly incorrect. If a user follows good practices for quality model development, he or she should identify the suspect elements by checking element quality before the run and taking appropriate measures. Additionally, a rigorous check on convergence identifies most problems related to distorted elements and corrects them with mesh refinement. Of more importance to the manager of an analysis team is the delay these meshing problems can cause. Depending on the tools used, these geometry issues can make the meshing process take much longer than necessary, or even shut the project down. If the FE users in a group have not made clean geometry a hot issue, most likely they have resigned themselves to the belief that difficulties generating a mesh are a necessary evil. They are not.

5.3.2 How Small is Small?

Typically, problems are caused by features that are an order of magnitude greater or smaller than the nominal element size specified. As a team learns to develop minimal geometry for validation, dirty geometry most likely is created unintentionally as features are created in the course of modeling. The examples shown in Figure 5-3, Figure 5-4, and Figure 5-5 are typical of the modeling errors that give meshers problems.

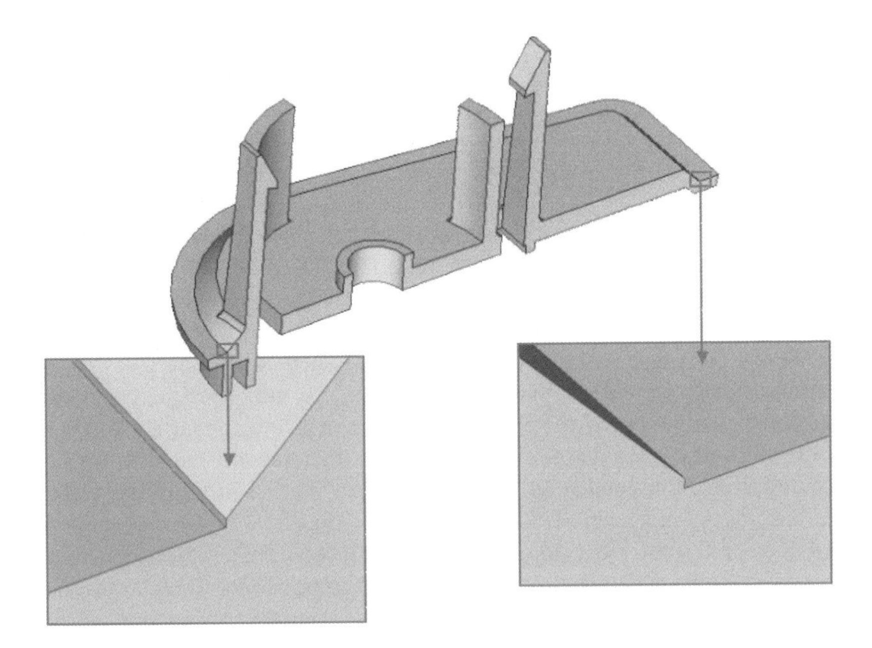

Figure 5-3 Sliver Surfaces Due to Rounded Dimensions

Figure 5-4
Draft Feature (Center of Image) Causing Sliver Surface with Near Zero Degree Angle

Figure 5-5 Assembly Misalignment Causing Sliver Surface

Unfortunately, there is no "silver bullet" for this problem, and the best solution is increased diligence by the geometry creators. Some CAD packages provide utilities to seek out small edges, and this can help if used regularly. However, the best bet is to investigate the edges created by every new feature for an unexpected inconsistency or discontinuity. As solid modeling packages strive to make their integrated analysis packages more robust, a handy feature would be a temporary layer that stores the most recently created edges and/or surfaces from an operation. A user could then toggle in and out of this layer to aid the investigation of feature acceptability. Another method of minimizing bad geometry is to make the meshing tools available to the CAD modelers. These designers could check the meshing robustness of the models periodically to catch a mistake as early as possible instead of building more geometry off a flawed base; this is much the same thought process as is validating designs with FEA while a concept is being developed.

5..4 Keeping Design and Analysis Models Common

The use of a single CAD database for all downstream tasks is very attractive for many reasons. The analysis model is always tied to the latest design. More importantly, changes based on the analysis results can update the design model. The down side is that to develop a CAD model that incorporates the needs of analysis, yet is still robust enough for downstream documentation tasks, may take longer than CAD simply for drawings. However, a reduction in delays due to confusion over revision levels would make up for this easily. Guidelines for solid element models and those that should utilize idealizations like beams and shells are discussed separately.

5.4.1 Solid Element Models

The most important aspect of developing CAD solids that can be used as both analysis and documentation databases is to start with the base features that control the performance of the part. If these are created first, rolling a model back to the base state with parametric links to downstream features should be relatively painless, and the goal of a master model is nearly attained. The second most important aspect of developing CAD solids is that of using a generalized dimensioning scheme to develop both these base features and subsequent features that might be used for optimization. Remember that dimensions that impose a concentric or parallel relationship are fast and easy to apply, but in some cases may not be consistent with an optimal design. The construction of CAD solids should anticipate the needs of design improvement.

Both of these guidelines imply upfront knowledge of how a part or system may perform. This should be relatively easy for evolutionary designs, but blank-sheet-of-paper concepts may require some test models to sort through the factors that affect performance before the designer embarks on the primary database.

5.4.2 Idealized Models

Keeping the CAD and analysis models linked for parts and systems that require idealization (i.e. planar, beam, or shell approximations) is a more difficult task. Certainly the aforementioned guidelines for developing solid models should be applied before the design team considers keeping a CAD model linked parametrically to an idealized FE model. Secondly, a good rule of thumb is to begin geometry development with entities that will facilitate FE model development. If a structure is to be analyzed using beam elements, develop a wireframe starting point that is called an envelope or a skeleton in some CAD systems, and use this to drive all subsequent solid features. This envelope should have all the information needed to develop the FE model. If the analysis model is to be constructed out of shell elements, develop the parts with mid-surface geometry that can be thickened into a solid as a separate feature. The important tie here is that the CAD model should be constructed so that it can be rolled back to the state that best facilitates creation of an FE model.

The better fit a structure is for a particular idealization, the easier rolling back becomes. Consider a large sheet metal weldment like a garbage truck body or a combine head. Constructing a mid-surface model in which the corner edges are coincident necessarily creates a slight error in the actual part size due to adjustments made for the absence of wall thickness. However, this error is typically in the range of tolerance for these dimensions anyway, and the nominal dimension on the print can be tweaked to account for the size adjustment. As the magnitude of these adjustments begins to approach significant feature size, a secondary operation can be employed, ideally in the context of the CAD assembly itself, in which the parts are trimmed to reflect the as-manufactured geometry. The example of a structural steel frame shown in Figure 5-6 illustrates this technique.

In the first two images, a wireframe envelope is constructed where beam elements might be located, typically the neutral axis of the element. The initial cross-sections are sketched in the envelope for reference. This envelope can be exported to an FE pre-processor where it can be meshed directly. Many FE tools can use the sketched cross-sections to derive the actual beam element properties. Once the design has been optimized, the solid parts are created in the CAD system using the envelope as a driving feature, and the overlaps where members connect are cleaned up using assembly features.

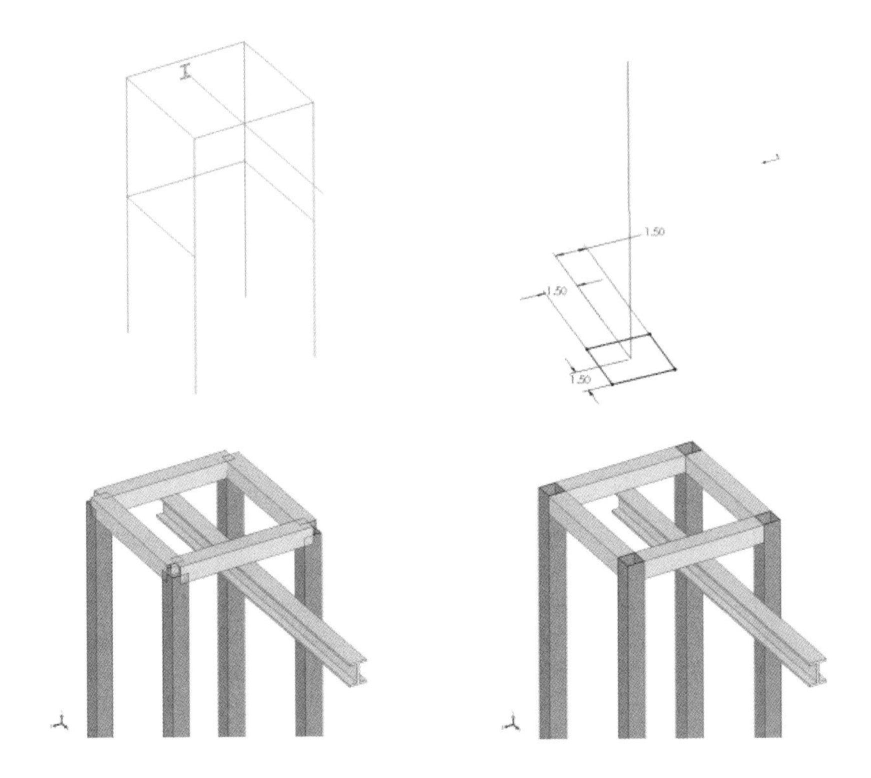

Figure 5-6 Developing Geometry for a Beam Element Model

5.5 Chapter Summary

The marriage of CAD and FEA is at times both a blessing and a curse. This union has enabled engineers to analyze complex structures that previously would have been impossible to analyze. It has also opened the door to thousands of new users among design engineers who otherwise would not have been exposed to the technology. On the down side, improvements in integration, translation, and meshing are tempting most of these new users and many who struggled with the old ways to over-develop CAD models. This inefficiency allows parts to progress further down the design path than necessary before their performance is validated. As meshing algorithms continue to expand the envelope of complexity on what can be solved, engineers and designers can push that envelope to the detriment of value and efficiency in the design/validation process.

A well-planned CAD/FEA program can yield faster and more innovative designs by allowing engineers to explore concepts at an earlier stage and by giving them automated tools that allow them to focus on optimal configurations. Making sure that everyone in the geometry "supply chain" is aware of the CAD needs of validation and the importance of avoiding feature bloat is one of the most important tasks a manager can undertake as he or she attempts to improve the impact that analysis can make on the design process.

6. Quality Assurance in FEA

Only a few years ago the subject of Quality Assurance (QA) in FEA was limited to analysis-centric organizations such as NAFEMS or internal groups at large organizations such as John Deere or Ford. Now the proliferation of the technology, its potential impact on the bottom line, and the growing awareness that bad FEA is worse than no FEA at all has forced the topic into the mainstream of product development discussions. However, given that companies range in size from global engineering organizations to local teams of five or six technical people, too few of them have taken serious steps towards controlling the quality of their finite element usage.

6.1 Why Control Quality?

When a company uses FEA only to double-check a design that was developed using traditional methods, the risk associated with a lack of FEA QA is minimal. However, many companies are espousing goals to drive design decisions directly from FEA data without having a clear idea of how to integrate technology into the design process or what type of QA is required. Achieving the goal of reduced testing or fewer prototypes must be preceded by a plan to target specific problems and challenges through analysis. That plan must include a QA program to smooth out the inconsistencies that arise from sporadic, intermittent, and/or uncontrolled use. Remember that a tool that is easy to use is equally easy to misuse.

A complete QA program must include testing designed to validate modeling methods as well as product performance. Additionally, the QA procedure must include an assessment of the skills and methods of the users and the level of responsibility that each user should be allowed—again, in a non-threatening manner. This assessment should not only identify areas of technical weakness but should also provide feedback on improvement options to bolster skill levels. Finally, the QA program should provide cross-departmental best practices and guidelines, such as pre- and post-analysis checklists and report formats so that users can learn from the work of others and the company's intellectual capital is used most effectively.

The successful implementation of a QA program should be accompanied by education of the management team as to the capabilities and limitations of the technology so that expectations can be properly set. Similarly, a comprehensive study of current tools and processes should precede and drive the development of such a plan so that goals and targets can be set with proper, company specific metrics put in place. Finally, a company must perceive that the development of a QA plan for FEA (a technology whose role in the company is not always clear to management or to the engineering staff) does not interfere with directives and programs that have higher visibility. The availability of an existing, yet customizable QA program from an outside source can alleviate the pressure a manager might otherwise feel in allocating precious internal resources to this task.

6.2 A Quality Assurance Program for FEA

The NAFEMS document "Management of Finite Element Analysis: Guidelines to Best Practice"[1] states that a quality assurance program should be developed to serve an organization, not vice-versa. To address this concern and the natural barriers that arise when attempting to quantify the expertise of people who for various reasons think their qualifications should be self-evident, a QA program must take into account the culture and history of analysis at a company so that it meets the needs of a wide-range of product development teams and industries. A QA program should include process audits, management education, user skill-level assessment, user education and continual improvement, pre- and post-analysis checklists, project documentation, data management, and analysis correlation guidelines.

6.2.1 Process Audit

The first step in establishing a QA program should be to document existing processes and company goals—including technical, organizational, and competitive goals. Developing an understanding of how products are developed, what the historical issues and challenges have been, what interactions exist, and how simulation technologies can best impact a company's bottom line should precede any recommendations. A process audit not only should evaluate the tools used by an engineering department, but also should identify additional state-of-the-art tools that can impact the design process or allow simulation activities to grow beyond current limitations. A process audit should help ensure that all groups involved in the design process are on the same page. Finally, the process audit should put some monetary values to typical tasks so that potential savings and opportunities for gains can be more readily identified. The report generated from the process audit should be a living document that allows periodic review of critical components and observations.

6.2.2 Management Education

A survey of users, conducted prior the 2001 NAFEMS World Congress,[10] indicated that management was the greatest barrier to success of FEA in product design, for a variety of reasons. Helping managers set proper expectations regarding the capabilities and limitations of analysis is often the single most important step in improving the quality and value of simulation at a company.

Management training should also include a discussion about the validity of assumptions and results and the concepts of quality control, with an overview of skills that they should expect their team members to possess if they are to be productive users of FEA.

6.2.3 User Skill Level Assessment

Assessment of skill levels may be the most difficult and controversial component of a QA program, as well as having the most far-reaching impact. Skill level assessment is not technically difficult, as there are several areas of expertise fundamental to the successful use of analysis. The difficulty lies in the potential for perceived threat. Consequently, users must be shown that the program is not a test, but a tool to help them understand their skills and needs better. One such program may include sections in which candidates do the following:

- Demonstrate a basic understanding of engineering mechanics (failure theory, stress concepts, material properties, etc.)
- Show a working knowledge of finite element analysis (terminology, concepts, capabilities, meshing, boundary conditions, etc.)
- Solve hands-on sample problems (using FEA tools that will be integrated into of their jobs)
- Present a personal portfolio of assessed past work (reports, screen shots, models, plots, etc.)

The assessment report provided to management afterward should include the candidate's performance results; an individual improvement plan, including courses and other support options, targeting any skills found to be deficient; and an endorsement of special skills the individual could share with others in the organization. Finally, there should be a positive evaluation of the user's level of competence and/or approved responsibility level. This should be free of negative connotations that could be misconstrued.

6.2.4 User Education and Continuous Improvement

A proactive and forward thinking QA program should identify the areas of growth and knowledge required to keep users' skills sharp. A company cannot be confident that users are using state-of-the-art techniques and tools unless they are exposed to people and techniques outside of familiar surroundings. NAFEMS workshops and conferences are excellent resources for this. The process audit conducted at the beginning of each program identifies critical skills and techniques needed to maximize the benefits of simulation. The skills assessment identifies users who need improvement in those techniques. Employee growth should be planned, not expected to happen haphazardly. Knowledge and documentation of the next plateau for each user or group of users, with clear milestones, helps to maintain quality. It is recommended that all users within an organization go through the same set of courses so that all are using the same language and have been exposed to the same data.

6.2.5 Pre and Post-Analysis Checklists

NAFEMS has developed an excellent starting point for companies looking to implement the use of checklists as a quality control tool.[1] These checklists should be customized to reflect a particular company's tools and analysis environment. As part of a total QA program, users within an organization should have these available, either on-line or as hard copy, as part of the project documentation, described below. Bypassing these simple checking tools can cause minor errors in data entry and interpretation resulting in major problems in the decisions made based on FE data.

6.2.6 Project Documentation

Too few companies have standard report formats for analysis, while many companies do not mandate reports at all. Despite the obvious loss of intellectual capital a company experiences when an analyst leaves the organization without documenting his work, when reports are not completed, a company loses one of the most important quality control tools in its analysis process. A QA program for analysis must include a report format that transcends groups, specializations, or departments. Analysis data on seemingly unrelated components could provide insight and prevent repetition of work. In addition to providing details of the recent work, a project report should include references to similar historical projects, test data, and correlation criteria. A report should indicate the source of inputs and assumptions, as well as comment on the validity of these assumptions. With the quantity of information that can be acquired and stored in today's environment, the source of information eventually leading to a design decision must be tracked and linked to that decision. Additionally, a company would benefit from linking test and analysis reports, especially if it used similar formats for the two related tasks.

6.2.7 Data Management

As companies begin to evaluate their Product Lifecycle Management (PLM) structures, the organization of analysis or other product performance data must be included in the initial planning. D.H. Brown and Associates have investigated the needs of Computer-Aided Engineering (CAE) data management and have found that structured Product Data Management (PDM) systems may not be up to the task.[6] PDM systems were typically developed to manage revisions and bill hierarchies, not the simplified geometries, results formats, and validation databases required for an analysis program. While every company must develop its own PLM and a data management system that best fits within its organization, a QA program for analysis must tap into that system, formalize it if need be, and provide means for managing the archives of analysis data so that a company's intellectual property and investment in simulation is secure.

6.2.8 Analysis Correlation Guidelines

Unfortunately, companies rarely correlate their finite element data with physical testing. When testing is used, set-ups are often inappropriate, proper procedures are not followed, and sufficient data points not gathered. Therefore, thought should be given to establishing multiple validation points to ensure that boundary conditions, material properties, and geometry are all properly specified to provide consistent correlation. The analyst and the test technician should work closely together to devise a test intended to correlate the analysis modeling assumptions. Care should be taken to evaluate the validity of constraints in the model, especially fixed constraints, as these can lead to gross variations in stiffness when comparing test results to analysis results. A QA program for analysis should bridge the gap between test and analysis and document procedures for correlating FE data.

6.3 Chapter Summary

No two companies operate alike, even if their product lines are similar. Consequently, if management assumes that a QA program is valid for all companies, it runs the risk of forcing its engineers to cater to the needs of the system. If nothing else, a QA procedure for FEA must provide a cross-check on the most likely sources of error—geometry, properties, mesh, and boundary conditions—as the key assumptions in any analysis. Ideally, all users in an organization possess all the skills required to perform analyses competently. However, as technology proliferates further into the design process—as it should—the likelihood of all users having this required skill level becomes less and less. Managers of engineering organizations need to foster a quality environment so that analysis can be used to its full potential. Remember, quality does not happen by accident. Only with planning, standardization, education, and diligent follow-through can a company truly feel confident in the quality of FEA. QA is also vital in case future problems with the design lead to any legal proceedings.

7. Justifying Analysis in the Design Process

Attempting a hard justification of FE tools prior to implementing them is akin to consulting a crystal ball. That upper management at many companies still requests justification in savings or additional revenue for the purchase of simulation tools indicates how poorly the technology is understood. While it might seem that a published post mortem evaluation at a competitor or company in a similar industry would provide some insight into the monetary justification for a company, possession of the technology is not what provides a competitive advantage, since most of the competition is probably using simulation as well. It is a company's ability to use the technology better than its competition that makes the advantage real.

Two major manufacturers in the marine outboard motor industry purchased the same simulation tool at about the same time nearly ten years ago. Today, one is still struggling to find a place for simulation in the design process, and while the engineers are passionate about the opportunity FEA presents, the management has never allowed it to become a driving force in their design environment. Conversely, the other company has grown an impressive analysis group, one that has branched into more in-depth tools and physics and uses simulation to build a noticeable market advantage. Theoretically, with nearly identical product challenges and similar geographic access to resources and talent, these two companies should be getting the same benefit from FEA. The difference is in management's commitment to it.

7.1 The Return

When considering an initial implementation of analysis, it is worthwhile to develop an idea about the potential for savings and areas where savings can be made. Eaton Corporation documented a 30 percent to 50 percent reduction in product development time and cost because of effective implementation of their up-front simulation program. They also documented a 12 percent to 24 percent Return on Investment (ROI) by using analysis tools at the initial stages of implementation.[7] Once training, software, and hardware costs are amortized and depreciated fully and the skill level of users improves, percentages can be expected to rise. These numbers are consistent with other studies published.

A Process Audit (described in the previous chapter) at the early stages of evaluation can be a great source for potential analysis benefits. If done impartially and thoroughly, a study of this nature can identify the "low hanging fruit" or the areas where a company can get the biggest bang for its buck. Utilizing this information and the statistics listed above, one can get a sense of the potential return on a properly implemented analysis program. A safety factor applied to this estimate would reflect management's anticipated commitment to the program. Use 1 if there appears to be a strong commitment to making simulation a driving force in product development, and 0.25 if management approves one seat of software and training for a couple of engineers with no commitment to restructuring the way products are developed.

While these numbers are good indicators, a soft, yet equally poignant justification makes the most sense in light of the impact utilization has on success. The consulting firm of Booz-Allen & Hamilton identified that 46 percent of all new product development costs go toward failures.[8] If half of a factory's output ended as defects, management would shut the place down. In the manufacturing process, an investment in new assembly or fabricating equipment can be justified with reasonable confidence that documented throughput improvements will translate into dollars saved. In engineering, and especially in analysis, this is not a sure thing. In the beginning of Richard Hamming's book *Numerical Methods for Scientists and Engineers,*[9] the author makes this profound statement: "The purpose of computing is insight, not numbers." This may be the biggest justification for implementing FEA.

Remember, however, that insight is not guaranteed either. One author on this topic has suggested that FEA always reveals some relevant aspect of a design. This is a dangerous misconception, because poorly set up models or poorly understood failure mechanisms can lead a user to draw conclusions with utmost confidence that are 180 degrees opposed to the actual situation. If an analysis is done incorrectly and/or the user does not know how to interpret the information, the time spent is, at best, wasted and, at worst, responsible for furthering erroneous design decisions. No financial justification should be made without an implementation plan to make good on those estimates.

7.2 The Investment

The other half of the ROI calculation is the investment in analysis tools, hardware, training, and the learning curve. There are many analysis software options and computer platform choices, but a comprehensive guideline for determining the right combination is beyond the scope of this text. However, a few general comments on the four components of investment are warranted.

7.2.1 Analysis Tools

With prices ranging from free to annual leases of $50,000 and up per seat, if cost is the primary driver (it should not be), it is possible to name a price and find software offered at that level. Elements to consider include CAD compatibility, a growth path for the analysis solver options (dynamics, nonlinear, Computational

Fluid Dynamics [CFD], optimization, etc.), available support resources, plans for growth of the technology within an organization, and integrity of the supplier. Do a real benchmark on a current engineering challenge, remembering that the demonstrator is most likely at a skill level much higher than that of current staff, and that one application engineer may be better than another at presenting a solution, even a lesser one. Focus on the quality of the results, the steps required to get there, and the openness of the supplier to disclose problems encountered when completing the problem. If a company does not have solid analysis experience to help sift thru the volumes of information, someone else must help make the decision. There are many professionals in the industry who can offer objective advice without a stake in the choice made. This can ensure a better choice.

7.2.2 Hardware

These days it is likely that most analysis is done in the PC environment. Many of the newest CAD integrated tools are available only on these platforms. The easiest method of justification for investment is the incremental cost of better hardware versus mediocre hardware. Too many analysts are handcuffed by inadequate computer resources. One company that truly needed to analyze assemblies could only analyze parts because a contact analysis drove their computer to its knees. It was not difficult to see that the number of hours spent wrestling with inadequate hardware easily outpaced the cost of an upgraded system. If there is a real commitment to using analysis in the design process and the decision is to stay in the PC environment, it is worthwhile in the long run to get the fastest dual-processor system with as much RAM as the operating system can recognize, as well as several times more hard drive space than the anticipated need. It really does pay off.

7.2.3 Training

Basic training is never enough. This topic is addressed in more detail elsewhere in this text, so suffice it to say that many studies have shown that training and education pays for itself. There are often economies in training many people at the same time. After the basic software training, customized classes based on a company's actual engineering challenges stick with users the longest. In addition to introductory training that teaches the interface, consider workshops that focus on the FE method and how it is applied to the design process. A user that truly understands the FE method can learn and be successful on nearly any tool.

7.2.4 Learning Curve

The worst time to make a commitment to simulation tools is at the exact moment they are needed. Down time is the best opportunity to minimize the impact of learning curves on productivity. Any supplier that promises a user that he or she will hit the ground running shortly after basic training is either not telling the truth or offering a tool that is too limited to do real work. Before tackling real problems, anticipate a ramp up period of one to several months, depending on the percentage of time spent on learning and the capabilities of the user. Having regular access to a coach or mentor—with the vendor, internal to the company, or from an outside firm—can increase the pace of learning by catching mistakes before they turn into habits. Also remember that proficiency with the software is only half of the skill set required to be effective with FEA. Users must also show that they have the requisite engineering knowledge to properly interpret and act on the information provided by the analysis tool. The Skills Assessment described in the previous chapter may help both management and designers to better understand the challenges that lie ahead in implementing simulation.

7.3 Chapter Summary

With the growing acceptance of simulation as a benefit to the design process and the number of major manufacturers committing large amounts of resources to the technology, one might suggest that the justification for it is self-evident. In reality, few companies are prepared to act on faith in that manner. However it is justified, remember that the benefits are only as good as the quality of use. Also remember that initial successes do not guarantee that future programs will be as successful. Sometimes success is user dependent, sometimes project dependent. It is worthwhile to continually evaluate and measure the use of analysis and to use these metrics to refocus, improve, and otherwise adjust use of technology.

8. A Manager's Role in the Success of FEA

It is reasonable to expect that readers' management styles range from hands-off to micro-managing a team. However, there are some common characteristics of managers who enable successful implementations of FEA in the design process, and a handful of guidelines that, if followed consistently, should help steer the use of analysis around the most common pitfalls and speed bumps. All managers need to help their users approach each simulation with care and discipline, a characteristic often overlooked in the pursuit of quick results, soon rationalized as valid. Additionally, a manager who has committed to making this technology an innovation driver in his or her organization must also establish and police the process to make sure design and validation are performed at optimal times for minimization of error and wasted effort. These two areas are the focus of this chapter.

8.1 Promoting an Analysis Culture

When applied correctly, FE-based simulation can deliver on the promise of reduced cost, accelerated schedules, and improved product quality. The testimonials from major industry, most notably automotive and aerospace, are numerous and readily available from any FE software vendor. What is typically downplayed in these success stories are the mistakes made en route and the level of training, QA, and correlation required to reach the point at which these successes can come readily. To help his team walk that path, where learning and growth may seem slow and often be frustrating, a manager must have an objective understanding of both the process and the users involved.

8.1.1 Supportive Scepticism

Regardless of the level of implementation at an organization, it is wise to remain somewhat sceptical about the use of analysis, especially on a program that does not build on earlier successes. Typically there is an abundance of over-confidence among the users on a team. The manager must embrace their enthusiasm without getting too caught up in it. An appropriate position to take is, "That's great...but did you check...," or "How can you justify that assumption?" or some similar qualifying question. In most cases involving new or part-time users, there is a leap of faith in the construction of the assumption set that may or may not be valid. Even users who are more experienced may succumb to poorly substantiated assumptions. This is not a negative, but a reality based on observations of hundreds of users. However, helping them discipline themselves to question and justify everything makes for much more robust, bullet-proof analyses.

8.1.2 Expectations for Users

At a minimum, users should follow all the QA guidelines established in accordance with Chapter 6. On a more general level, an organization most likely has users at different skill levels. A common statement made by beginning or part-time users is that they are only concerned with "quick and dirty" results and do not need to go into the same level of detail that a full-time analyst or consultant might. This comment is typically made in defense of a poorly thought out or justified assumption. **It is extremely important to remember that while FE experts are expected to have all the answers, ALL users must ask all the questions**. A casual user may not know how to model an uncommon boundary condition, but he must realize that this boundary condition is needed. Similarly, a design engineer may not feel he has time to explore all the extents of his assumption set within the context of a tight project schedule, but he must still comment on the anticipated sensitivity of his results to the extents of this assumption. Failure to do so makes it difficult for the manager to determine if he even was aware that he was making that assumption. Finally, it is best that everything be documented in the project report, either for posterity or for the unfortunate circumstance in which legal proof of diligence is required.

8.2 Removing Roadblocks

FEA is only PART of the process; without top-level buy-in and commitment, it cannot achieve its potential. This commitment goes beyond purchasing the software and budgeting some training. The technology needs to be positioned within the framework of the design process. Suggestions for this make up the earlier chapters of this book. For this to be successful, management needs to break down the barriers the engineering team runs into and give the users the opportunity to perform the work they have been trained for. In addition to the suggestions made previously, a manager needs to make sure that all users have the hardware resources they need and access to mentoring and support. Managers also must help police the process that enables analysis to impact the bottom line

8.3 Final Summary

The partnership of CAD and analysis has gone a long way toward making FEA more accessible to more users. However, there is a growing concern that availability has outpaced education. Responsibility for proper usage ultimately falls into the laps of the users and their managers. Management involvement can make or break the success of simulation as an innovation driver and a competitive advantage. It is necessary to make adjustments to the processes in order to take advantage of the insight and opportunities that will arise. Management must promote a culture of excellence in which users are not satisfied with poorly structured assumption sets or engaged in engineering concepts beyond their backgrounds or skills. A set of standards, best practices, and QA procedures can be pivotal in making sure analysis corresponds to a high degree of excellence. Remember, though, that calling something a best practice does not mean that it is. Methods need to be constantly questioned and updated to adjust for changing skill levels, software capabilities, or simulation needs.

Managers of a simulation-enabled engineering group must get involved in the technology. They must be prepared to walk their teams through the slow parts of a learning curve while challenging assumptions and results. Helping users stay focused on the end result, an improved product or process, can make choices clearer. Most bad analysis can be traced back to bad engineering choices and decisions. Regardless of management's knowledge of the technology, remembering that engineering judgment can explain nearly all questions regarding modeling and results interpretation should enable any manager to bring his or her analysis implementation to its full potential.